About the Author

Sarah is a mum of three children from Glasgow. When she saw her dad, Bill, exhibiting signs of dementia, she decided to spend as much time with him as possible, while he still knew who she was. From a close family with her dad at the helm, she knew that time was of the essence and upon losing him, decided to chronicle the whole family's journey. This is her first foray into writing, although having studied history and politics at university, it is something she has always loved.

Because I Know Who He Is

Sarah Smith

Because I Know Who He Is

Olympia Publishers
London

www.olympiapublishers.com
OLYMPIA PAPERBACK EDITION

A CIP catalogue record for this title is
available from the British Library.

ISBN: 978-1-80074-504-9

This is a work of creative nonfiction. The events are portrayed to the
best of the author's memory. While all the stories in this book are
true, some names and identifying details have been changed to
protect the privacy of the people involved.

First Published in 2021

Olympia Publishers
Tallis House
2 Tallis Street
London
EC4Y 0AB

Printed in Great Britain

Dedication

For Dad and all those who suffer and have suffered, and for all my wonderful friends at Erskine who cared so beautifully for him.

Acknowledgements

To my family who supported me and still do today, thank you. I couldn't have done it without you and certainly couldn't have written this book without your love and encouragement.

Prologue

I remember the day clearly when I knew for sure, albeit instinctively, that something was wrong with my lovely dad. It was early January 2017. My brothers, Ainsley and Bruce, and I had noticed dad was repeating himself and often forgot things we had spoken about and recently done.

Three years earlier we had taken him to the memory clinic for tests. He passed all but one with ease, so I suppose since then this had been a 'slow burn'. We had suggested he returned for more tests as time passed, but he steadfastly refused. Perhaps he knew himself all was not right.

Dad lived on his own and had done so since our mum died in 1996, so we wondered initially if it was loneliness and he just liked to chat about the old days. But no, this was something greater than that.

On that Friday I had popped round (which I did often) to see him with my dog, Lottie, whom dad loved. Although I had a key to the house where we had grown up, I had stopped letting myself in as I had noticed it scared Dad if I did, preferring instead to ring the doorbell. He answered the door with a big smile on his face… he had a lovely smile… "Hi Dad, how are you?" I greeted him. "Fine thank you," he replied.

We sat and chatted. I made him coffee and he ate the strawberry tart I always bought for him and then we started to look at old photographs. It was then that he asked me "Who are those people?" pointing to photos of Mum and my brothers. My heart sank. I told him who they were and then I asked "Who am I, Dad?"

"I'm not sure," he admitted.

"But you let me in everyday, Dad. Why do you do that if you aren't sure who I am?"

"Because you say 'Hi Dad,'" he explained.

That day marked the beginning of a six-month fight to persuade our lovely daddy that he needed help and a realisation for us that this incredibly intelligent man was suffering from dementia.

Foreword

Bill Mann was the most extraordinary person. As a young man growing up, he was an ever present in my life, someone who had played cricket and rugby for the same club as me but in a previous generation. The New Anniesland clubhouse had many team photos adorning the walls, and there he was, immaculate and intense in many of them. A Mann for all seasons if ever there was one.

Those team photographs are still there. They will never be removed.

Intense is very possibly a good word to ponder at this point as even as a young man I knew that a conversation with Bill would take me to places nobody else went. If I was ever brave enough to talk to him, I would pretty soon find out my weaknesses, and where things were going wrong. All with a glint in his eye, as if he was testing me.

We all knew he was a successful businessman but I, for one, had no idea about his philanthropy at that stage. Nor that his future actions would generate millions for good causes and sports and that he would protect the very fabric of some of our most precious Scottish cultural assets.

Bill gave to charity, he helped orchestras to tour, he helped businesses with a leg up, he spent time with youngsters, he had a drive that was immeasurable and admirable, and he would give of himself to those who could never possibly copy him.

What set him apart, for me, was that his charitable giving was about giving away huge amounts of money but in small chunks to little charities for whom it made a massive difference.

A Mann for all seasons with time for everybody. Truly a one off. `HIs legacy is extraordinary. An amazing man.

John Beattie

Foreword

I arrived in Scotland in the summer of 1979 to start my first professional cricket assignment. It was a time in my life when I experienced a mixture of uncertainty over events within my own country, South Africa and excitement about my sojourn abroad during our winter and off-season.

My association with Scottish Cricket started with the Poloc Cricket Club in Glasgow and then, even before that season ended, being selected for the Scottish National Team to play against Australia.

It was at that game that I met the late Bill Mann in his capacity as President of Scottish Cricket. I still remember the game very well because it was my first ever international appearance, not having been able to do so in my own country as South Africa was banned from competing in International Cricket because of the apartheid policy of the then Government

After the game I was informed that the President, Bill Mann wanted to meet with me. As a fairly newcomer to Scottish Cricket, I didn't know what to expect. We sat outside in a very casual setting and after introducing himself to me, he asked me a few general questions. He followed this up with immediately telling me in no uncertain terms where he wanted to see Scottish Cricket in the near future. I still didn't know where the conversation was heading and was quite jolted when he abruptly told me that Scotland wanted me to start that journey with them on the field of play.

All I did was sit and listen. This was the last thing I expected. I was completely dumb struck. I recall taking a deep breath when he asked me if I would be prepared to take on the assignment. I explained to him that I had a three-year contract with Poloc Cricket Club, to which he immediately replied that that would not be an issue. I also recall telling him that although I was definitely interested, I would need a few days to think about it. He simply pushed ahead with his pitch and said that Scotland would offer me a five-year contract and that I would be able to finish my three-year commitment with Poloc Cricket Club. I walked away from that meeting and for days I was on cloud nine.

It was a lot to digest… I was battling with the turmoil and the uncertainty back in my home country, and the prospect of never being able to represent my own country because of the Sport boycott against South Africa… along comes this guy, Mr Bill Mann, President of Scottish Cricket and offers me this unbelievable opportunity… Wow!

The fact that he gave me a five-year contract with Scottish Cricket gave me an enormous amount of confidence and self-belief. It is no secret that this opportunity turned my life around and I ended up staying on for thirteen years.

Cricket ran deep in the Mann household my relationship with the Mann family didn't just stop at the end of my playing days. Years later his son Ainsley also contacted me from China to assist him with women's cricket.

Bill Mann... a remarkable man, a man of action. A visionary leader that was very clear and firm. Looking back, I see him as a transformational leader and in my mind, well ahead of his time in terms of where Scottish Cricket was at that point. He certainly walked the talk.

He was able to instil passion, love, and determination in people and that speaks volumes. He certainly left a lasting impression on me and my family. I remain forever grateful to him, and I can only count myself extremely fortunate that our paths crossed.

I will forever treasure the memory of meeting up with him again after many years. He was ill at the time but we had a lovely long chat about cricket.

Omar Henry

Chapter One
Dad

Billy/Bill Mann (or W M Mann CBE as he became known) but to us, plain old dad, was born on 22 November 1934 in Dalmuir, northwest of Glasgow. The second child to Thomas and Helen Mann, wee brother to Tom and big brother to Ellis. I always remember my granny telling me that dad was a very contented child right from the start; rarely crying and always at his happiest when he had a ball in hand, and so this would continue all his life... he LOVED sport, particularly cricket and rugby. He was evacuated during the Blitz and despite the dementia he could recall those days clear as a bell; going to school on his dad's motorbike with his sister sitting on the fuel tank! Post war the Mann family moved to the West End of Glasgow. In so doing, beginning dad's love for that part of town and setting him on the road to do everything he could for that community. Barring a stint in Malaya for National Service, he lived there for the rest of his life.

It was clear early on that dad was gifted in maths, so he trained to be an accountant and worked for two big firms before he started his own business, which still runs today under the watchful eye of my twin brother Bruce.

Dad spent his free time playing rugby in the winter

and cricket in the summer, always enjoying a beer or two afterwards with his teammates and this fostered his love of the clubs of which he was a member. I remember our childhoods were spent watching him play at Accies and also West of Scotland Cricket Club.

In 1963 he met our mum, Aileen. Mum was very attractive, glamorous and very outgoing. Dad was actually quite shy and didn't really do 'small talk' so the combination of the two worked well... mum brought him out his shell and dad's love of community and clubs rubbed off on mum, who was always watching on the touchline beside him or in the clubhouse making the teas! They married soon after on 12 April 1964 after our grandpa Thom wisely told mum "You will never meet a man better than Billy Mann." Dad always had a very sweet nature and I must admit to being his 'princess', as my name suggests. Coupled with that, dad had a very quick wit and his piercing blue eyes always had a twinkle in them, either for fun or telling you he was one step ahead of you... which also prompted his friends and those who knew him to say 'everyone who knows Billy Mann likes Billy Mann'... I think if we can live our lives with people saying that, then we have done something right! Ainsley, our big brother, was born in March 1966 and Bruce and I followed in March 1969. Ours was a very happy childhood spent playing and watching sport but playing with our friends too. I was told once if you don't remember anything big in your childhood then it was a good one and this was certainly true of ours.

And so it was, life continued, dad always seemed to have his head in accounts of some form; rushing into the house up the backstairs because he was five or ten minutes late for dinner, hoping mum wouldn't be too cross! What I didn't realise at the time was by the late 1980s he was pretty much retired, preferring to put his energies instead into good and/or charitable causes. This he did by the 'bucket-load' supported by our mum when they set up the W.M. Mann Foundation in 1988, with a single donation of £25,000. That amount (with other contributions and careful management) has grown to be worth £9 million! Two thirds of the income it generates is given away while the rest is reinvested. The reason I am telling you this is because I am so proud of my parents' generosity of spirit; believing that once you have a certain amount you should give back. Mum passed away from cancer in 1996 and dad busied himself in good works for the rest of his life, often anonymously too. There are so many people and organisations that my dad has touched; in either turning them around because of his financial acumen and brains, or campaigning for a cause that he believed in. He and a friend Alex Kilgour, managed to persuade a Thatcher government to abolish VAT on sports club memberships and only levy rates in the bars and restaurants of sports clubs, (which in 2017 was estimated to be worth in excess of £3 billion) prompting one commentator to describe dad as 'the biggest indirect funder of sport in the UK'. WOW! That's my dad! In December 2017 dad was quite rightly appointed CBE for services to sport, recreation, charity and the arts, and as a family we couldn't have been prouder.

My dad adored my mum and although their marriage

was cut short, it was clear to see the love they had for one another. Dad always told me that the last couple of years of mum's life were so special to them as they made time for each other, either at home or abroad, because they knew time was short. My mum passed a month before my first child Molly (and their first grandchild) was born... that was hard for us all, but little Molly brought so much love and light into all our lives at such a dark time. Dad really stepped into the grandpa role beautifully, probably much more so than he would have had mum been alive. He always used to say to us that when Bruce and I were babies, if he saw our curtains open when he came home from work, he would nip to the pub! Changing nappies wasn't his thing! Eighteen months after Molly came Max, and three years later came Rosie. They were the light of his life; always watching hockey and rugby matches with me, giving advice and sometimes it was only grandpa's voice they would listen to as awkward teenagers! That bond was so special and dad's illness and passing has been awful for them. We all miss him so much. Five other grandchildren came: two boys for Ainsley, Ali and Agung (it means mighty I think, in Indonesian). Dad travelled to the far east every year to visit until he no longer could, so they came here. Bruce has Griff and funnily enough, twins like us, Ffion and Rhys. 'Funny names' I hear you say, well Ainsley's wife is Katarina, who is Indonesian and Bruce's wife is Carys, who is Welsh! Dad always joked that because he had a 'brr' (i.e., he couldn't say his 'r's') we all gave our kids difficult names for him to pronounce!

So yes, my/our dad was a very clever, hardworking,

generous man known in fact as 'The Numbers Mann' in two busts of him in Glasgow by the acclaimed sculptor, Archie Forrest. But it was his family who meant everything to him, and none of his achievements would have been the same without his love for us and our love for him... our lovely dad.

Chapter Two
A Moment of Crisis

It was 3.43 a.m. on Tuesday 21 November 2017(I remember it so clearly because dad's eighty-third birthday was the next day) when my phone rang. It was dad. Never had he rung me in the middle of the night before and he wasn't making any sense. Yes, he rang me repeatedly during the day when I wasn't with him, but not in the middle of the night... It still amazes me that he could dial my number at this stage as he didn't have a mobile phone, but it just shows how his brain processed numbers. I rolled over to Simon (my then partner) and said "It's Dad... this is it... the crisis moment... I'm going to him."

Bruce and I had been waiting for and dreading this moment in equal measure. I called to tell him what was happening and made the five-minute drive (at that time in the morning) to Dad's house where Bruce was waiting for me, as he lives just up the road. He looked at me (paperwork in hand... just like Dad, he is always organised) and said "What are we going to do?" I looked him straight in the eyes and said "We are going to get him out of there."

For the last six months I had been going most days to see Dad; buying him food, making sure he ate, doing his washing and simply keeping him company and all the while trying to persuade him he needed more than I could give, but he resisted any offers of permanent help. Before his illness he had always said that in his dotage he would employ a live-in chauffeur and housekeeper to look after him, but this was one illness we hadn't factored into the plans. Thankfully (also years before his illness) he had given Power of Attorney (POA) to us, proving what a sensible man, he was. It was something we never wanted to use and, if I'm honest, didn't think we would have to use. Thus, Bruce carrying paperwork that night.

Bruce had said to me often that because I did so much for Dad, he himself thought he was OK (as do most dementia sufferers) and they are very good at 'masking' any issues… giving you an answer that makes sense but it is not the right one. For example, I would ask "What did you have for lunch today, Dad?" and he would always reply "The usual" … but on checking the fridge and bin I would discover nothing had been eaten. But one day a crisis moment would come, and we would step in…early morning on Tuesday 21 November was that moment.

We rang the doorbell and moments later there was Dad beaming from cheek to cheek; so pleased to see us, fully dressed. It was then I realised that he didn't sleep at all. I knew he found it difficult to tell the time (a common indicator of dementia and in the winter the long dark days make it even worse) so I had bought him a speaking clock, but even that was hard to fathom for our dear dad. Bruce and I hugged him and went into his study where we chatted idly for a bit. Dad was happy. The mood changed though when I said it was time to get help and go to hospital.

A week previously I was phoned on the Saturday morning by a neighbour, saying Dad was out in his pj's asking what the time was. Understandably Dad didn't want to go to hospital, but he needed to., We didn't know what else to do. As Bruce called an ambulance, I tried to calm Dad down and had a coffee with him. As I put the cups in the kitchen, I saw out the corner of my eye, the front door open and Dad leave. I grabbed my coat while Bruce stayed on the line. Dad was so distressed and frightened of me. I kept a discreet distance so as not to inflame the situation any more. For someone who had sore legs when he walked any distance, boy he could walk fast! It was late autumn and the pavements were covered in leaves. I was frightened he would slip. But then the ambulance appeared. Still keeping my distance, I let the paramedics deal with Dad, who wanted nothing to do with me. They spoke calmly, repeatedly calling him Bill which seemed to help in turn calm our wee dad. By this time Bruce had appeared. We were on the phone to Ainsley in Jakarta, telling him what was happening. Ironically the paramedics told us although we had POA, they could not force Dad into the ambulance against his will.

After much discussion, Dad stepped into it. To our relief, because his blood pressure was high, he agreed to go to hospital... providing I didn't go with him! That wasn't easy for me to take — but as long as he was safe then that was the main thing.

Bruce and I returned to Dad's house to pack a bag and lock up. When I went into the bathroom, I noticed a bath had been run... I checked the water; it was scolding hot... that was the first of many tears realising what might have been.

Sadly for Dad, there had been a bad influence in his life in the previous eighteen months or so. Suffice to say this person (a woman) told Dad we were making up lies and that there was nothing wrong with him. She cancelled doctors' appointments and even managed the unthinkable… to turn him against us… his own children… his 'Twinnie Bins' as he called us. Strangely, when she wasn't there his attitude to us softened, but when she was, he was adamant… he wanted nothing to do with us.

However, she underestimated our love for our dad and our determination to get him help. Bruce and I (always supported by Ainsley from afar) resolved to do so and that's what happened that cold November morning. As upsetting as it was for one and all. Thankfully, I knew she was not there that night, which made us all the more determined to act.

I didn't realise it at the time, but Dad was never to return to his home of thirty-six years. His home where he was so happy for so long; where we grew up from the age of eleven, where he loved and cared for our mum, where he welcomed new grandchildren and looked forward to their visits but was denied the chance to leave it in a calm manner. I hate that we did that to him, but we had no choice and I learnt often over the next two years and one month, that there were lots of hard decisions to make, decisions that no child (no matter how old) wants to make for their parent. All of those decisions stemmed from that 'crisis moment' but they were all made with love, as painful as they were. Dad needed professional help, we needed help and help is what we got from that day on.

Chapter Three
The Snow Globe

Dad spent his eighty-third birthday in hospital. We had cake and coffee, and for a moment he was relaxed. But it wasn't to last for long. He could not understand why he was there, why I had 'done this to him' and what must have seemed like (although it wasn't) constant questioning from strangers. He could always reel off his birthday when asked and told stories of men being in his house using it as a place of work. He had told me this several times and at first, I questioned it, but then realised it was less distressing for Dad for me to go along with it. It was in fact word perfect every time. He recounted it always ending that they had reached an amicable agreement that the businessmen could use one room every day, but must leave by close of business! This may sound strange or not even resonate with you, but it WAS Dad's reality and still his business mind was whirring, which made me smile. Any questions he couldn't answer were met with the same response each time… "They asked me something I'm not interested in," he would say!

This was a familiar pattern each day; me trying to distract him from constantly asking me why he was there and when would I take him home?

There was a major event looming however and he

knew it. On 15 December he was due to receive his CBE. We had arranged months earlier that it would be in Glasgow as we knew travelling to London would be too much for him. Dementia sufferers don't like a change in routine and environment, even if to the rest of us it's upside down. I spoke to all the doctors and said regardless of what was going to happen moving forward, I WOULD keep my promise to Dad that he would receive his CBE. They agreed, albeit some reluctantly. Brain scans followed with yet more questioning, until after two weeks Dad was taken to the dementia unit of the same hospital, The Queen Elizabeth Hospital in Glasgow. I was so nervous... what would he say? Would he even notice?

I tried my best to be strong but inside my heart was breaking... which it was to do often over the next two years. The answer was 'yes' he did notice! But I managed to bluff my way out of it by appealing to his giving nature, saying that someone who was really ill needed his old bed, and this was his new (but of course, temporary) one! God I was getting good at this lying thing. But like most things I learned that it was OK to tell wee white lies if it made him feel better.

Langlands, as it is called, is a 'locked ward' for obvious reasons and although somewhat tired, what it lacks in style it makes up for in kindness and love. I learnt there that those people; doctors, nurses, carers, domestics, whoever, are the most wonderful people I have ever met. Surprisingly to me, Dad seemed quite happy there and then the penny dropped... he had constant company and care. He didn't have that at home, just Bruce and I popping in and oh, not forgetting Lottie!

On the Sunday I came to visit Dad and noticed all the swing doors were shut inside the ward, which was unusual. I asked the staff what was happening. Well, my wee dad had come to 'the aid' of some female patients who, in their demented state, had told Dad they were being kept there against their will; they had husbands and children to care for. Dad promised them he would sort it for them and led the chant "We want out!" I had to laugh and told the nurse that I was sorry for any trouble he had caused but that was Dad… he always led campaigns for people and causes he believed in. I was so very proud of him that day as he still retained a sense of self, in the midst of all the black clouds.

In that moment, I knew that the care homes I had visited and the one I had picked out for Dad (with a massive sense of betrayal) was the right thing to do.

Eventually, after nearly three weeks, we received a diagnosis… of sorts. Dementia is the umbrella term and there are many forms of dementia. It was decided that, after all the tests, dad was suffering from fifty/fifty Lewy bodies dementia and Alzheimer's. I had heard of the latter but not the former. Lewy bodies is often highlighted by hallucinations and paranoia (both of which dad suffered from). It can be and often is, more acute and lifespan-shortening than say vascular dementia.

Being a Pisces I cried, sobbed, my poor daddy. But I was also frightened as I knew very little about dementia. I collected my thoughts, pulled myself together and cuddled my wee dad. While we waited for Dad to get a room in the home of our choice, Erskine Glasgow for veterans, we had five days where Dad stayed elsewhere as his bed in Langlands was now needed.

Clarence Court was at the bottom of my road and had good inspectorate reports, but Erskine was just that little bit better and it sounds silly I know but had more male residents. Dad was always a 'man's man'(Mann) so I felt it would suit him better.

So, Dad did receive his CBE on Friday 15 December. We all went as a family in our best bib and tucker. I'm not sure he fully understood everything that went on that day, a cruel irony of him receiving it years after his peers and friends felt he should have, but I think you will agree his smile says it all!

The very next day we took our lovely dad to The Erskine Glasgow Home… saying only we were going for a cup of tea to see where some of his donations had gone.

How do any of us tell our parents they can no longer make their own decisions because they don't have the capacity to do so? That job fell to us.

Little white lies…

The title of this chapter refers to an analogy I was told by Harry, a dementia nurse who, when I was bubbling and crying; saying how guilty and sad I felt when I realised that Dad needed full time residential care, simply said "Think of it as a snow globe… what happens to a snow globe?"

I said, "The snow falls upside down and makes a mess."

To which she replied, "Yes it does, but it also settles and that's what will happen here… you are making big changes but all for the better and in time, life will settle down." I thought about that, and it did make sense to me and indeed I still think of that often. It helped me see once more that hard decisions are often the right ones because you love your parents… I see that now, sometimes you have to shake that snow globe.

Chapter Four
Erskine

Bruce had gone ahead to sort Dad's room, while Ainsley and I had taken Dad out for lunch (thinking wrongly we could 'soften the blow' somewhat). We all piled into my car and drove to Erskine. After a few minutes Dad asked the dreaded question "Where are we going and when can I go home?" Ainsley, who although a very successful businessman, left it to me to answer!

"We are off to Erskine, Dad, for a cup of coffee to see how they have used your donations." But there was no fooling our wee dad... he didn't want to go. He must have suspected something.

On arrival we were met by Ewa (a Polish Senior Care Assistant) who I was told was excellent at her job and would take control of the situation, having dealt with new residents often. She was bright and welcoming but also had a sense of authority about her. But in a kind way... I wasn't wrong there! More on Ewa and the other wonderful staff later.

The rooms at Erskine are comfortable and purpose-built for dementia. They are bright with skirtings and edges painted in bold colours because dementia affects everything, including your sight and perception. Each room has an en-suite big enough for wheelchairs and hoists when the time comes. Dad was 'lucky enough' to have a room overlooking the garden courtyard. I say 'lucky enough' because he didn't feel lucky that day, bless him. He did sit down and accept a cup of coffee but all the while maintaining he would not take off his coat and neither would he be staying for dinner. Ainsley, Bruce and I looked at each other both with despair and sadness, but we all knew in our hearts this was the right decision. I always said, and still do, that if you are going to end your life in residential care, (never liked the phrase care home), Erskine is the place to be. All its communal areas are open-plan: the sitting room flows into the dining area and each floor is called a 'house'. Dad was in Linburn House. The continuity of care is second to none. Some of the carers have been there since it opened in 2007 and some, like my friend, Karen, have worked for Erskine for over thirty years... that speaks volumes to me. I must point out that Karen was not my friend, nor were any of the staff until we first met there, but they are my good friends now and I feel privileged to call them my friends.

There are three houses in Erskine Glasgow... Flanders on the ground floor, Linburn on the middle and Mitchell on the top, housing forty-seven residents in total. Not everyone there has dementia, but most do – all of course at varying stages. I must admit to being quite taken aback initially with some behaviours, but this was only because this was a world I knew nothing about.

Ewa quickly saw that us being with Dad for too long would only make his initial transition worse, so gently hinted that we should go home. My dad's blue eyes didn't leave me... he didn't want me to leave. In a way it's like dropping your child off on that first day of school or nursery... you know it's better to be kind but firm. Ewa assured us Dad would be fine and I knew he would be well taken care of, but would he really be fine? Left alone with strangers... abandoned by his children... I gave Dad a massive cuddle but he wasn't so keen... a practice I was to experience often during his illness until the last few months. Never did I judge or question him... it was simply his illness, not my dad as I knew him. Of course, he was confused, frightened and angry and I completely understand that. Every day thereafter was all about trying to make Dad's life as happy and with as little distress as possible. And so began the journey we took together, negotiating the problems this disease throws at you — both as a sufferer and a relative.

I drove home with a heavy heart, but I knew from the visits I had made to Erskine when choosing it, that all the residents are not only cared for, but loved by all the staff — doctors, nurses, carers, domestics, and admin staff - and for that matter, other residents' families. Some of the 'guys' living there had done so for years and some were new like Dad, but I had only ever seen kindness, patience and love for one and all (even if not all the residents felt the same every day!) I called Ewa later that evening to be told Dad had eaten everything for dinner and had had seconds (he always had a great appetite!) and had happily chatted away to the other guys. I keep using that phrase I know, but I mean men and women. I soon learnt we were all just a part of the Erskine family... and, unusually for a family, it was one that didn't fight, just one that supports and cares for one another… in my book that's a pretty good one.

So I knew that night when I went to bed that Dad was safe, warm, well fed and cared for and should he not sleep once more through the night, he would have company; someone to watch TV with, someone to chat to and (as I was to learn the next day) someone to have tea and sandwiches with when he just needed to be fed again! I also knew this wouldn't be easy for Dad and if I'm honest I had no idea how difficult it would be for me, because of my ignorance of dementia. But I also knew that with the guidance of everyone at Erskine we would never be on our own taking that journey. That knowledge allowed me to sleep properly for the first night in ages.

Chapter Five
A New Way of Life

It was for sure a new way of life. Not just for my lovely daddy, but for me too. We were both grappling with this awful diagnosis and Dad living in Erskine. I don't really think that, although I knew this was to be Dad's new home, l really thought it was to be his final one, spirited away from everything that was familiar, (even through the clouds of dementia) living with strangers — some of whom who were further into their 'journey' than Dad… and he recognised that.

As I walked with Lottie to visit him the next morning, it was a Sunday, I too did not realise that this was a journey I was to make most days (give or take the occasional week here and there) for the next two years. I arrived with a great deal of trepidation. How would Dad be? How would he respond to me? Would I be strong enough not to cry? As anyone who has ever had to take the decision that the time has come for a parent, spouse or sibling to go into residential care knows, the feeling of guilt and failure is overwhelming.

Dad greeted me that morning with equal amounts of love and antagonism. He was so pleased to see me but equally wanted to know when he was "getting the hell out of here". The one question I always dreaded. I cuddled him and distracted him with Lottie, who he adored. We talked about the room, how lovely it was, and the day's activities. Erskine have a fabulous activities team who lay on two activities a day for all the residents, covering a wide range for everyone's different interests. But really the only thing Dad wanted to know was when he was going home. His suitcase was packed and he was ready. This was to continue for eighteen months. Looking back, if I knew that day that was how it would be, I don't know if I could have coped as I did. I'm not saying there weren't tears (mine and his) but sometimes not knowing what lies ahead is a good thing.

Dad always had a sweet tooth so I was always armed with sweeties, cakes and biscuits and I soon realised that he would devour enough food for a week, overnight. Slowly, it dawned on me that he wasn't conscious of the quantities he was eating but also because he did not sleep (which is not uncommon for those suffering from dementia) he operated pretty much twenty-four hours a day. I could never understand how he kept going but I suppose knowing Dad as well as I do, he had steely determination in everything he did in life, and this was just another battle to fight.

Usually after long persuasion, I could take him to an activity, often with the promise of a glass of wine! Some he enjoyed more than most. Dad was never one for small talk, conversation had to have purpose; business, sport, or family... I wouldn't want to say which was more important!

Interestingly one of the activities he did enjoy was music therapy. In his 'previous' life he could take or leave music. Mum loved it so he went to concerts (not pop concerts but classical or choral) with her, but this he did enjoy. Like everything else it was very interactive; singing, playing instruments. To see people come alive was wonderful for me. Every activity we were always accompanied by Lottie. The pride on my wee dad's face when everyone wanted to stroke her was a joy to see. I soon learned all the old songs from Dad's and the other residents' heyday, rather shameful that I didn't know more to begin with.

I marvel at the love and kindness shown by Bette, Donna, Tommy and Jack (not just to Dad but to everyone in these activities) and indeed all the staff at Erskine. It also showed me that actually I was so fond of all of them too and I was keen to learn more about this disease and how best to respond to and deal with it.

Rugby memories was also an activity Dad loved. They would watch old matches and chat about them. He was in the winning club side in Scotland in 1954 (on the wing for Accies) and he talked about that constantly, so this was just up his street!

So some days were better than others, but one thing was always constant – his refusal and/or dislike for me leaving. I used to dread saying that I was leaving. Rarely did I say I was going home as I understood very quickly that this was a 'no-no'. Can you imagine telling your parents who have dementia that is OK for you to leave but not them? Instead, I would say that Lottie needed to be walked. "When will you be back?" Dad would ask and, depending on how he felt, there never seemed to be a right answer — an hour… no, way too long, half an hour... same again, and then we would engage in a twenty minute or so discussion on my leaving. I felt quite strongly that I would always say I was going and always kiss him goodbye — something I learnt to do when Molly, Max and Rosie were wee whenever I went out at night. To me it made no sense to wait till they were asleep and then leave them with a babysitter, no, they needed to know Mummy and Daddy were going out so, should they wake up, they weren't surprised that we were not there. So I took the same approach with Dad but by God it was easier with the kids! Dad's brain, although dementing (that's the phrase that is used for anyone who may think I'm being politically incorrect), was still sharp in that he could argue a somewhat confused point and if I wasn't quick enough on my feet, the discussion could go on for ages and cause upset. I would usually stay until dinner time which was five p.m. so I could walk Dad to his seat and the staff could reassure him. If I could not stay that long I would ask him if he wanted to watch a rugby or cricket match. This was something he always wanted to do. It didn't matter that it was a DVD and we had watched it countless times before, as he had forgotten he had, so we would settle down together to watch it. On a good day he could become so engrossed that when I got up 'to walk Lottie' he would be happy enough and give me a cuddle and pat me on the head as he had done since I was a wee girl. I took those days and departures with a sense of happiness. They set me up for my visit the next day.

So we carried on as best we could with our new life. There were lots of fun moments; partly because of Dad's sense of humour, partly because some of the things he said or did were funny and he laughed too. There were lots of loving moments too, mixed in with angry, frustrated dad but I was always OK with that because I had got my relationship back with my daddy. I wasn't his carer any more, I was his daughter once again. Yes, our relationship had changed from 'pre dementia', but we could go to activities, watch TV or a film, look at the old photos and simply spend time together and that was good enough for me.

Chapter Six
A Duty of Care

The world of dementia was entirely new to me and although at times it frightened me, I wanted to know more and learn everything I could to try and understand it, which would in turn allow me to understand Dad more.

Instead of settling into Erskine as I hoped, he was becoming increasingly antagonistic and sometimes aggressive towards me. The incessant questions regarding when we were going home, what time it was, when was lunch, dinner etc were taking their toll on me. Bruce was always at the end of the phone when I left to go home to speak to and Simon, my lovely partner, was always waiting with a hug on my return. It was hard for Molly, Max and Rosie too as I wanted to protect them from what was actually happening but at the same time, they saw me upset and they also wanted to see their grandpa.

I realised quite quickly that Dad thought we (him and I) were living in a private members' club abroad, and to dispute this was not only pointless but in fact cruel. He had plans for our departure wherein he would sell his house and we would live in a smaller property happily together, with Lottie of course!

One day it was all too much and I sat and spoke to Tracey (one of the senior care assistants) and cried my eyes out. She told me not only do they have a duty of care to each resident but also to their families and to let it all out. That was a lovely moment for me and to everyone because I realised, she and all the staff at Erskine, meant it. Not only was Dad suffering but we were too. When I asked how on earth to deal with it, she simply said I had to enter into his world as he believes that to be reality. It seemed so obvious looking back but I hadn't thought about it before. Instead, I had been correcting him on the old stories or even questioning what he had told me he had done that day... how could I have been so cruel and stupid? So that's what I did and encouraged everyone else to do the same, it DID make life easier. Yes, wee dad's suitcase was packed every day without fail and yes, he asked every day when we were leaving, but I was better equipped to answer his questions and telling a wee white lie was OK as it kept him calm(er!). I quietly unpacked the suitcase when he was in the loo or told him I needed to tidy up his room and most times I 'got away' with that. Dad would ask me if my room was as nice as his (he knew I had children so accepted I would need a bigger room to accommodate everyone) and when I appeared mid-morning and he would ask where 'the hell' I had been (Dad never swore pre dementia) I would simply say I was with the kids.

Trips out were not successful, even to his beloved Accies or The Baths. Don't get me wrong, he enjoyed them at the time but returning to Erskine was always very difficult. He would become very upset and angry, and I never did it alone. Eventually I decided the joy of lunch, rugby etc was outweighed by the distress it caused returning to Erskine, so any trips thereafter would only be with the Erskine team and on the Erskine bus. That was a sad day, as I recognised I would never have Dad in my home again or do the things he really loved together.

We spent hours, pouring over old photographs and I am talking really old; Dad as a baby, some albums only going as far as his first eighteen months. He was a lovely baby I think you will agree. He actually taught me some family history that I didn't know and I always found that amazing.

Going back to the duty of care, when I asked the staff, my friends, why it was that Dad could remember so far back but not five minutes ago, they explained that the brain has 'layers of sand' – which are the most recent memories, going right down to 'layers of concrete' – the oldest ones. The layers of sand erode but the layers of concrete remain the strongest. That made perfect sense to me. It was a lightbulb moment. So what if Dad didn't know the time, the day, my name even? I did, and what he DID know was history and our family's history for that matter.

I learnt so much from him and all the staff at Erskine, and indeed the other lovely residents, and I feel so fortunate to have been able to do so.

In April 2018 that duty of care for me really came to the fore. Simon, and I had gone to Dublin for the weekend and on the first night, my lovely Si proposed to me. I was so excited and of course accepted immediately. On my return to see Dad, I was advised it probably was best not to tell him, his heart would break as he believed he and I were married. I look very much like my mum and I'm sure because we were so close and saw each other every day, Dad thought I was Mum. I was devastated. Never did I think I would meet anyone after my divorce (and certainly not someone as lovely as Simon) and to think I could not share my happy news with my wee daddy who had been beside me always, but more so in the last few years, was just awful.

However, I respected their opinions and the last thing I wanted to do was upset my dad, so I didn't tell him. Dad knew Simon prior to his illness, not for long, but he did know him and equally Si got to know my dad, which will always be special to me. Dad liked Simon, particularly as he too loves cricket, and always when he visited that was their conversations. It made me very happy. Selfishly, I didn't think at the time how Dad's decline affected Simon, but it hurt him too; seeing this super intelligent, high achieving man slowly but surely lose his faculties. I say Dad liked Simon (and he did) but as the dementia deepened, he was also jealous of him! Dad really just wanted one on one time with me always, and if Si went to the loo or to get a drink, dad would ask "Who is that guy?" Somewhat reluctantly I would answer "That's my friend Simon, Dad." Dad needed to hear that because I now understood that to tell him the whole truth, would devastate him.

That duty of care allowed me to have the strength to visit Dad each day, make wedding plans but I had no idea how I could get married without Dad, who remember was still alive, living ten minutes down the road from where we were getting married. As the time drew nearer, I saw for myself that for Dad to even attend would be way too much for him; he didn't like noises (another side effect of this disease) and crowds were a definite no. Our wedding wasn't big — forty-seven people to be precise — but forty-five too many for Dad! He was starting to decline and it would simply be too much for him. Simon and I visited the day before, and rather sweetly, Dad was in good form, allowing me to leave with relative ease. It's almost as if he knew I deserved this happiness. I was so worried how he would be without me as we were going to Spain for five days for our honeymoon. All the staff assured me he would be fine. I hoped so.

On Friday 5 October 2018 I woke early (three thirty a.m. to be precise), I was so excited but I was also sad — no Dad at the wedding. However, I thought about it that morning; Max was giving me away, Molly and Rosie would accompany us down the aisle, Bruce and his children had made the wedding cake and to top it all, Simon would be waiting for me! I decided no more tears that day, this after all, was Simon's day too. Dad would want me to be happy, and I was, I am, it was the most wonderful of days surrounded by family and friends and

I carried not just Dad, but Mum in my heart too as I walked towards Simon.

The love and care shown to me always during Dad's stay in Erskine was second to none, but at that time I really did feel their duty of care for me.

Chapter Seven
The Wee Girl with the Dog

I was so looking forward to seeing Dad when I came back from our week's honeymoon that I burst into tears when I saw him. Simon and I had a wonderful time, but it was long enough to be away from my wee daddy.

He viewed me with suspicion when he first saw me but once I hugged him and took his hand, his face lit up. The wee girl with the dog had come back. On speaking to the staff, I learnt that dad had asked constantly for 'the wee girl with the dog'... "When is the wee girl with the dog coming back?" It made me sad that he could not rest until Lottie and I had returned... even not wanting to shower or change. Dad's reliance and love for me was clear for all to see and indeed his relief that I was now back 'living with him in the private members' club abroad'. One of the things as I say you learn to do and is acceptable to do, is to tell wee white lies if that's what makes the person suffering from dementia, calm. For Dad it was so important to him that we were in this together! Any absences by me were explained by saying I had to walk Lottie, that my children needed me and so on. To tell him the truth would have hurt him, and so every day I found ways to think on my feet to answer his endless questions about when we would be leaving. If Dad asked me if I had a car I would say "No, I sold it Dad, as I walk everywhere," as even as he was rapidly dementing, his mind was still thinking about how we could leave and move into our own wee house together.

By this time Dad had been in Erskine for ten months and as Christmas approached, I could see the change in him. His speech had become very pressured and he was unable to complete sentences. In essence, he really struggled to have a proper conversation. However, we did spend hours 'talking' because it is so important to make your loved one feel vital, loved and make them feel that they ARE making sense. Dad always said that I was great at talking and actually, I am glad I am because it really helped us both to navigate the twists and turns of this disease. This was something that upset me so much at the time as I was not prepared for it. I thought dementia was simply a loss of memory... not so, and many times I thought to myself 'if only that were the case'... it robs the sufferer of everything, not just their ability to remember things like we do. It takes the ability for instance, to make the connection between cutlery and eating, so when Dad saw a knife and fork, he didn't know what to do with them. Something so simple, something he had done probably from the age of one... totally forgotten. Once prompted, he could pick up his fork or spoon but as this wretched disease progressed, he forgot completely.

We spent many hours looking at photo albums over and over again. The ones he loved the most were of him as a young man playing rugby, school photos and even ones of him as a toddler and I must admit that I loved doing that too. As a twenty or even thirty-something, I suppose we don't take much interest in our parents' lives as youngsters themselves, so I loved chatting and learning about his childhood. He could tell me all about his chums who lived in the flats around him in Falkland Street and how they all played cricket in the street together for hours.

As Dad's dementia worsened, I soon realised that when he asked me when he could go home, that the home he meant was his childhood one, not the home we had lived in as a family and he himself had done, until that awful day in November the previous year. The layers of sand had indeed eroded. Moments like that hit me hard. How on earth could Dad not remember Mum? How on earth could he not remember where we lived, the names of his children, and so on? As my understanding of the disease grew, I too understood that sadly this was just part of it and once I had completely entered into his world and his understanding of it, the easier it would be for me to cope with. Yes, it hurt, yes there were and still are a lot of tears, but this wasn't about me, it was about making life as easy and happy as possible for Dad. He loved Lottie: giving her treats, cuddling her and funnily enough he found it easier to remember her name than mine. I was 'the wee girl with the dog', often introducing me as such to other residents. He couldn't quite place me as Sarah or his daughter. So when people asked me why I visited every day when Dad didn't know who I was, my response was always the same… "Because I know who HE is." I know he knew I was someone special and that was good enough for me, Dad was still my dad — different, yes, but still the dad who had cared for and loved me unconditionally all my life. That is why I visited every day, because I knew who he was.

Christmas Day 2018 dawned. Molly, Max, Rosie, Lottie and I went over in the morning to see Dad. He was wearing his favourite jumper which I had given him two years previously, and I think you can see from this photograph how happy he was to have us all there. Erskine always made Christmas as special as possible for all the residents and their families: bright and cheerful.

By this point, as I said previously, Dad's conversation skills were hampered and each of the children dealt with it differently. Molly sat and chatted quietly to her grandpa and Rosie talked non-stop, but I don't remember Max saying much at all other than "Merry Xmas, Grandpa, and giving him a hug. All three lived away from home by then and their grandpa's decline was clear to see. They adored him, he had always had all the answers and solutions for any problems and now he was less able. I gently reminded them that he was still the same man, slightly altered, but still the same man and I know they knew that, but I also know how painful it was to witness their beloved grandpa changing in this way. It was my job to be honest with them, but also to reassure them he still had a sense of humour, he still liked to chat about the things he always had and most of all, he still loved them and he still loved a cuddle. After that visit I decided they shouldn't visit grandpa on their own, it was too upsetting, but also Dad now needed the reassurance and guidance of 'the wee girl and the dog' whenever anyone came to visit.

Chapter Eight
A Beautiful Mind

As I witnessed the 'wheels coming off' more and more with Dad, I had to adjust how we spent our time together. As I mentioned earlier, his ability to not only hold a conversation but to speak was becoming more compromised. 'The Numbers Mann', so-called because of his brilliant mathematical business brain, had lost the ability to count. Dad always had a back pocket full of cash and we always made sure he still had some (usually about £40) as it mattered to him that he still had that sort of independence and I truly believe he still knew the value of a pound! Bruce and I, told him his daily newspaper was free, something Dad delighted in as he 'pre dementia' supported Erskine as a donor. On one of my visits early January, he was checking his pockets for his cash (as he often did) when he asked me how much was there. It was two £20 pound notes. He couldn't recognise them as such. My heart sank again, my wee daddy didn't recognise cash. The funny thing was that although he had cash, Bruce and I had to tell him that everything at Erskine was free: accommodation, food etc as he would have been mad that we had to pay for anything. Dad invented a wee system of his own to 'pay' for his food, whereby he would collect the paper napkins from the tables and they would be his 'vouchers' for his meals — so simple but I also thought it incredibly sweet. He was never one to accept 'freebies', as he put it, believing them to be unethical. Sometimes it would take us up to half an hour to prepare for a meal, checking and double checking he had his vouchers and enough of them to pay his own way! Dad also hated wasting money so if ever I had problems persuading him to go for a meal I would say "But Dad, it's been made for you and someone has put a lot of time and effort into it". More often this was enough to persuade him! He also thought that 'the bars and restaurants were not busy and badly run'! To which I would say "You are good at sorting out businesses Dad, why don't you sort them out?" It was little skills like this that I acquired to allow conversations to flow but also to make Dad feel important and relevant. This not only meant so much to him but to me too.

Similarly, we were watching cricket one day about that time when he asked me if he had ever played it. Boom! Another dagger through the heart it seemed. Dad had played cricket from the age of eight. He captained his team in Malaya during National Service, taking great pleasure in telling his General he would be number seven in the batting order! He was a former President of the Scottish Cricket Union. How could he forget all of this? No one had prepared me for the depth of cognitive failure, but in a way, I was glad. It seemed easier not to know the minutia of this relentless, hopeless disease. Of course I knew there was no cure and that Dad would ultimately die from it, but I think if I knew exactly what was coming (and at this point setbacks were commonplace) I do not think I could have coped with the enormity of the situation. Instead, we took it one day at a time and tried to make the most of our time together.

I realised the layers of sand had indeed been eroded and we were now down to the concrete. Such a simple analogy but it was unfolding before my very eyes. More than anything else I had to learn to accept that and deal with only the concrete, for Dad's sake if nothing else.

Another issue Dad was experiencing was that his feet and calves were extraordinarily swollen, (because he paced up and down so much) to the point he couldn't wear shoes and socks. We bought him especially large ones but even they did not fit. He seemed to suffer constantly from cellulitis (which is common in older people as their skin is so thin it's very prone to infection) and if you couple that with a disliking for personal care, which Dad had, it can be very serious. Fourteen months into his stay at Erskine, Dad was still not sleeping. He would walk the corridors constantly and this was not helping his feet and legs. Although Dad had 'demented' he had not given up the fight and if I am honest, I do not think he really ever did until all the stuffing was taken out of him in his final few weeks. You see, Dad did not believe he was ill and it was certainly a very fine line to tread because he needed to know and understand he needed care, but also, I did not want to take away his dignity. My way of tackling the feet and leg issue was to tell him he would not be playing rugby on Saturday if he didn't rest! Dad was always telling me he had scored a try that day and it was a good game. I was of course 'delighted' for him — this was his reality and I too had to live it. Dad wasn't even using his bed so Bruce and I bought a luxury leather reclining chair for him, persuading him to rest, even for a bit, so he could 'play' at the weekend! I also employed a podiatrist to come in and do Dad's feet. I don't think he would mind me saying that even as a young man his feet were not his best feature! Bizarrely he actually enjoyed this so I took her lead and creamed and massaged his feet, in a bid to get them elevated, and he would fall asleep. Lottie and I would sit for an hour beside him in silence — if I made a move to get up, he would open his eyes... so I learnt not to, because he slept like a butterfly.

We discovered the joys of channel eighty-one, Talking Pictures, thanks to Andy (a fellow resident), all old films going as far back as the 1930s. Dad loved them as once again, he was taken to a time he could remember and relate to. As for me? Well, I just loved to see him smile and laugh. Those were good days.

The not so good days were those where he would look at me and cry, his blue eyes shining but tear soaked. I would take his hand and ask him what was wrong. His response was heart-breaking; he didn't know what was wrong, but something was. Amongst all the confusion, he knew something was not right and I could also see he did not know how to fix it. My feeling was that yes, life was becoming a struggle but deep down his mind was still fighting and he still had a beautiful mind. I always told him that. You see, I truly believe that those suffering from dementia (even those quite advanced like Dad) still have an awareness of what is going on. Not all of the time, but sometimes. I could see the way peoples' faces lit up when they saw Lottie; they would reach out to her, some who rarely spoke petted her and even sang in the music therapy group each week. It was a wonder for me to see. There were even times when I would be explaining something to Dad, mistakenly thinking he did not understand, when he would say "I know that!" And by God, by the look in his eyes I knew for sure that he did and that made me so happy. His beautiful mind was still there.

Chapter Nine
Billy the Dog

Billy came into our lives completely out the blue, but what a joy he was. He was a battery-operated pet therapy dog! Strictly speaking 'Sandy' was the first one to be honest, but on seeing Dad's connection with 'Sandy' and his reluctance to give him up, I resolved to buy one for Dad of his own. When Dad first arrived at Erskine I did see quite a few residents with dolls or teddies. I had never seen this before and I probably did stare, I am ashamed to say, as is it DID seem strange to me — these old people in leather armchairs on wheels, cuddling and speaking to their toys. Of course what I did not know then was that as the dementia progresses, the patient regresses and becomes more childlike. Like a back to front Benjamin Button! So of course it is perfectly normal to see those at the advanced stages of the disease, playing with toys. For some with vascular dementia the process can take years, but sadly for Dad with Lewy bodies, it was really quite rapid. I think it was at this point, March 2019, that I was totally 'on board' with who Dad was and what his needs were. He was an eighty-four-year-old toddler. I didn't shy away from that fact but it did not make me love him any less, in fact, probably more. He always wanted Billy with him (incidentally I assume you know why the name

Billy... Dad's childhood name is so easy for him to remember) whether it be at activities, lunch or merely sitting perched on his knee or with Lottie, on his bed. Yes, I saw newer residents' families staring at us as Dad shuffled along on my arm with Billy in the other. Yes, I saw them staring as Dad fed him crisps or I offered him a piece of cake, but this was our 'new normal' and it made Dad so very happy. He had Lottie and Billy now, he was so proud. Often Dad would look to me for reassurance that his care of Billy was good enough, proof again if ever I needed it, that my lovely daddy was still here. People often say that as a relative of someone suffering from dementia you grieve as they go through the process, and to some extent this is true but I for one, never totally lost my Dad as I knew him, honestly, I did not. I truly believe that once you enter their world completely, it is so much easier to cope with and your parent or spouse is still there inside. And so it was that Dad loved and cared for Billy so beautifully it made me proud, to the point it made me cry. Dad was still Dad and Billy had brought that out in him. I was going to take Billy home with me the night that Dad passed but decided instead his rightful home was at Erskine, where once more he would be cared for and loved by another beautiful mind with dementia.

Chapter Ten
Spring to the First Leaves of Autumn

By the spring of 2019 the deterioration in Dad was clear for all to see. His mobility was poor, he needed aid in walking, his speech was very poor (beyond the point of making any real sense) and he was becoming quite withdrawn. He was never one for small talk, but I could see that he knew he wasn't really able to hold a conversation, yet I knew instinctively what it was he wanted to say. Simon always says I smile with my eyes, Dad talked with his. We would sit every day and I would read the paper to him — something HE had done every day of his life and something he still did, except it was me doing the reading. Mondays were always good days in terms of all the sporting news I could impart, but even then, I could see he was less interested than he once was. He would always smile when I talked about Molly, Max and Rosie.

Dad really stepped up when my mum passed and he took a really active interest in my children's lives. He did however, always draw the line at changing nappies as babies! I remember I left him in charge once, overnight, of all three of them when I was going to Edinburgh for a girls' night out. Realistically it was Molly who was in charge! She must have been about seven, Maxie five and a half, and Rosie two and a half. I told her the only thing grandpa had to remember to do, was to put Rosie in her night-time pull ups. I left about five thirty that evening and was home (after a very late night) mid-morning. I rang the doorbell, Dad opened the door; hair unbrushed, glasses squinted and said "Oh thank God you are home!" Poor dad, I think he had barely slept — all three kids had but he was up to ninety with the responsibility. Molly, Max and Rosie were fed, clean and happy — what more could I want? Job well done I would say. Needless to say, Dad slept for a bit that day and it was a really long day for me! I often retold that story to him with photos of the children at that age. Reminiscing is such an important thing to do with someone with dementia as it's the 'old days' they remember, and we are all fortunate that we have so many lovely memories.

Dad built a house in the tiny village in southern Spain called Periana. He went several times a year but the children and I went every summer with him for twelve years. We often talked about those holidays and one of my favourite photos of Dad with the kids is this one,

taken amongst the olive groves on his land that first summer. He loved it too and it took pride of place on his windowsill in Erskine.

Soon the falls started to happen. Sometimes he would just slide off his seat, other times falling from his bed while just sitting there. Walking was becoming increasingly difficult, and I realised that he was needing a wheelchair — another hammer blow, not to him necessarily, but to me.

Dementia removes the ability to do everything. The brain simply disintegrates so you forget how to walk, talk, eat, toilet and so on. Again, I did not realise this at the outset but the more I read and learned, the more frightened I became of what was to come.

The carers at Erskine had of course seen it all before and they guided me through the sadness tenderly. Always cheerful, always looking to support me and when they had the time, they would sit with us chatting. Being a 'man's man' Dad was particularly fond of Alan. Alan is a big cheerful soul, he always called dad 'Bill Mann' — something Dad loved as that is how he was known most of his adult life. Alan loves sport, particularly rugby and when he had time, he would chat to Dad about it. Life is about the small gestures not the grand ones and one thing I did notice is that all the staff got to know who each resident was at the core and 'zoned' in on their interests. They were all treated as individuals, with such love and respect.

With dementia often comes behavioural problems. Some people swear, some can be sexually less inhibited, and some can be angry and aggressive. All very difficult things for families to observe and live with, but one of the many beauties I believe, of residential care, is that your loved one is being cared for by experts who understand the disease and have the coping mechanisms in place and patience to do so. You are giving your loved ones the BEST care possible when the time comes for them to enter residential care. Dad had the latter behavioural problem. He did not like personal care one bit, and it did become a balancing act in keeping him clean but also keeping him calm. Remember, Dad thought we were living in a private members' club abroad; that the carers were waiters (they brought him his meals, after all) so why on earth were 'the waiters' trying to shower and change him? It made perfect sense in Dad's head and when I thought about it like that, it did so to me. Some days I would say to the guys "Don't worry about it, let's just leave it for now". They were always so worried because they had a duty of care to Dad for his personal care but also understood it caused him such distress.

Lottie and I would distract him that summer by sitting out in the garden on the balcony, chatting about the flowers and colours. A sense of proportion can become lost on a dementia sufferer so Dad would often think a tree or plant was much bigger than it was, but he liked his time outside, nevertheless. I would push him to activities with Lottie and Billy, but I could see he was becoming more and more withdrawn. He used to love a glass or two of wine but no longer, sounds silly I know but even that made me so sad.

I had stopped all visitors by now other than family and his two best friends of sixty-odd years. Mr Guthrie (even today aged fifty-one I still call him that and not by his Christian name, Colin, as he tells me to!) Dad and Mr Guthrie had been rugby teammates, the latter being the elder of the two. Their wives became great friends and I don't remember life without them. Mr Guthrie became Dad's lawyer but he was just in fact his best friend, and he and one other, Mr Scott, came to visit religiously. I was always there too as I knew it was so very difficult for them to see Dad deteriorating in this way. Most older people are frightened of dementia, I understand that, but not those two. In spite of me saying often they did not need to keep coming as I knew how sad it was for them, they never faltered in their friendships with Dad. I will always be so grateful to them for that. I couldn't help feeling a sense of abandonment sometimes for Dad as so many had forsaken him (many of whom HE had helped over the years, most of whom did show up at his funeral) but I couldn't help thinking how much it would have meant to Dad for them to be there in life for him. Dementia is an incredibly lonely and isolating illness if you let it be. I do hope that changes sooner rather than later.

Another big downward milestone was double incontinence. Yes, this disease strips you of all your dignity but it is restored in some way by the loving care of the carers. It starts slowly with the odd accident here and there (even just a timing issue like toddlers) but like the rest of this relentless disease, it takes over. I clearly remember the day I first went to buy 'adult pull-ups'. I couldn't quite believe it had come to this, but once again I snapped myself out of it. This was about caring for Dad with love, respect and dignity and that was all that mattered. He didn't seem to notice the change in underwear fortunately, but once more he resisted changing them and sometimes it just had to be done. It was the moment I was dreading; cleaning up my lovely daddy in that way — selfish I know, but I too, was scared. We were all trying to persuade him as calmly as possible to let the carers change him, but he wasn't having any of it, until he pointed at me and said "She will do it." Alasdair the nurse asked me if that's OK by me, I simply nodded and aided by him, I got on with it.

Dad was calm and he allowed us to do it together. The professionals have it to a tee, so it is as stress-free as possible. Dad was clean, fresh and nicely presented as I bought him lots of lovely shirts, polo shirts and jumpers so that he always looked cared for and loved (as were all the residents by their families). Just because you are incontinent and suffer from dementia doesn't mean you can't look smart.

I walked home that day in tears. My sadness was for Dad that life had come to this, remember I didn't 'pick my nose without asking him first!'... he often joked about that... But I was also proud that I had crossed that massive emotional hurdle and I could now tend to all of Dad's needs whenever he needed me to.

Ainsley came home to visit Dad late September, just as the first leaves of autumn were falling. I prepared him as much as I could for the decline in Dad, being honest, but I hope kind too. But honestly nothing prepares you until you see it for yourself. I know it was a shock and also so very upsetting for him to see Dad have 'an accident', but that is one of the things that happens when suffering from dementia and perhaps by then I had become accustomed to it. To his credit, Ainsley stepped up, getting clean clothes and so on but I know it was painful to see in the flesh. It was something Dad never got used to right up to the end. He could be aggressive and angry, he hated being changed but somehow when I could hold his hand, talk to him and just be with him, it seemed to help. This is a terrible thing for a parent to have to go through and a child to witness but the truth was that Dad had become a child, and you wouldn't think twice about caring for a child like that, would you... so why would you with an elderly parent?

Dad and Ainsley spent a lot of time together that week. I think Ainsley knew he may not get another chance. This was the second time he had to make that lonely journey back to Scotland and then back to Asia, knowing he was saying goodbye to his mum and dad. It

 must have been heartbreaking, but they both had a mutual love of cricket so whiled away the hours watching it and talking about it. I deliberately tried to keep my distance that week, allowing Ainsley the time with Dad that he needed. He took this photo of him on the last day and it is one that makes us all

smile; Dad in his MCC hat smiling — Ainsley's last memory of him, I think that is a good one.

And so as the first leaves of autumn started to fall, Dad entered the darkest stages of his suffering.

Chapter Eleven
Saying Goodbye to Grandpa

By early to mid-October Dad was no longer able to walk, toilet, speak properly or even eat solid foods. He also had to be hoisted from and to the bed. The cot sides were up to stop him falling out of bed. He was completely physically incapacitated. His PIR was on constantly to monitor any movement in bed, and he slept more than he was awake. His brain was rapidly disintegrating, and I knew his decline seemed to be speeding up. He was eating 'nursery food': soups, mashed foods and ice cream. The days of him being able to enjoy a biscuit or sweetie or even a cake, had gone. As the disease progresses the throat closes over making swallowing not just difficult, but dangerous. He needed to be assisted eating. I and the guys would spoon feed him and/or break little chunks off a sandwich or a sponge cake and pop it in his mouth. This was something I did without hesitation and looking back a year later I'm surprised I did not find it more upsetting. Maybe it was because he would just look at me with his sparkling blue eyes, so full of trust, accepting it himself. I think that was the time that I knew that Dad could no longer fight this cruel and hopeless disease, one he had done so for so long. I think also that there are so many cognitive and physical failures by this point, that you as the carer/relative just focuses on learning how to deal with it for your loved one. What I did know for sure was that I had to give Molly, Max and Rosie the opportunity to say goodbye to their beloved grandpa before the disease completely ravaged him.

I called them all in turn and told them the stage we were at, and I felt that now was the time to come and see their grandpa before he became any worse. Molly, as usual, had lots of questions: how did I know that? How long? But they all had the same one question, was grandpa OK and comfortable? And of course, he was.

So it was that they all came home for the weekend early November. Max does not cope well with things like this and I saw the pain in his eyes when he came to see him before he went back to university in September, so I was at pains to say to him that he did not need to come home just because the girls were. He did of course decide to do so. That weekend we visited Dad many times. It took so much out of me; I think I cried the whole weekend. Rosie kept wanting to go back to see him, I understood why, but it was so painful. Dad slept most of the time, but she was her cheery self, talking non-stop!

Molly went twice and sat beside the bed holding his hand. At one point she dissolved into tears, falling on his chest. The reality was just too hard to bear. Poor Molly, she was heartbroken, but do you know what? My wee dad was able to comfort her by gently patting her back and this he did with Rosie too. They were upset that they had broken down in front of him, but I felt on the contrary. I was so very proud of Dad, to still be able to sense their upset and comfort them. That for me was, and is, a very special memory. We left for home later that day and that equally is a horrible memory; sadness, sadness and more sadness in their faces.

Max was yet to visit Dad, but I also knew he was going back up to Aberdeen later that day and I didn't want him driving in the dark while upset. I told him it was time to go. I could sense his reluctance but equally I could sense his need to say goodbye properly. As we were leaving, he said "Is Lottie not coming? You always say grandpa is better when Lottie is there." I wasn't going to take her to be honest, but I realised Max needed her to be there, a sense of hope and comfort I suppose as she had always been. I knew then that either Maxie didn't realise how ill his grandpa had become or maybe more to the point, he didn't want to face up to it. Once again, I got it. Maxie, Rosie, Lottie, and I went into Dad's room. Immediately I could see the tears well up in Max. I tried my best to chat to Dad, telling him Maxie was here but it was no good. After five minutes Maxie wanted to leave. He could not bear to see his wise, kind, funny grandpa like that and that was OK by me. I did however tell Maxie to hug him goodbye, knowing he would regret if he did not. He said his goodbyes, I walked him up the corridor and we both sobbed into one another. It was horrible but I know that all my lovely children were so glad to be able to spend the time — long or short — with him and actually very brave I think to do so, and to say goodbye properly.

Max drove to Aberdeen, Molly returned to London and Rosie came home with me before going back to Aberdeen the next day. That weekend was so terribly sad, they and I knew they would never see their grandpa again.

Chapter Twelve
The Road Home

22 November 2019 was Dad's eighty-fifth birthday. I had organised a wee tea party for him with myself, Bruce, Simon, my cousin Katie and all the lovely residents in Linburn, and not forgetting Lottie of course! Molly and Rosie had written the most beautiful cards telling their grandpa what he meant to them, heart-breaking but lovely nonetheless. I read them out to Dad who by this stage had such a terribly sad look on his face, almost a blank expression, but as I did, he began to cry.

I hugged him tightly. I know he understood the love that came from them and indeed the love from his family, but we felt the love from him too. Dad cherished those cards. He had them beside him always from that day on, either placed in his hand by me or on his lap. Alan (one of the carers) gave Dad a squeezy ball knowing Dad's love for ball games and that too stayed with him. I even named it with a love heart around it. We all sat and chatted to Dad and one another.

Hearing is one of the last things to go so it is so important to include your loved one in the conversation. Katie had made a cherry cake (Dad's favourite), which she had done often over the years. This birthday however, Dad couldn't eat the cherries for fear of choking, so I broke tiny wee bits of sponge off and fed them to him. Although he couldn't speak, I know he loved having everyone there and he looked so smart in his new pink jumper I had bought for him.

Soon everyone left and it was just the three of us. But one of the lovely things about Erskine is that you are never really alone. As other families came in to visit their loved ones, they came over, wished Dad a happy birthday and spent some time chatting with us. As far as birthdays go under those circumstances, it was a good one; Dad was surrounded by friends, family and love. Not all elderly people have that — so many spend it on their own.

The days passed. Dad was sleeping more and more. December dawned and I could see things were deteriorating. I had already done all the Christmas shopping, wrapped the presents and ordered all the food by the start of December. I guess you could say I had a sixth sense as much as I did not want to admit it. Simon told me later that week when he last saw Dad, he asked him how he was, to which he replied "I'm ready." Never did he say that to me, to spare me the pain, I'm sure. Dad was no longer really eating much, the odd bit of ice cream or soup but he would let you know that he had had enough by closing his mouth tightly. Liquids had also become a problem as they can be a severe choking hazard which is mad I know, but if you think about it, sometimes when you take a drink it can go down the 'wrong way' — that's the effect in the very late stages of dementia because the throat closes over entirely. To combat this, you add thickener to any drink and the sufferer can take it from a spoon. Again, news to me but that is what we did. I did discover that Dad had a taste for a certain up-market Italian lemonade — a slight upgrade from his Scottish brand (no offence to that well-known brand!)

Simon had downloaded the chart music of 1964 (the year Mum and Dad met) to listen to, so we did that and I talked about Mum and his mum and dad, and his brother, Tom and sister Ellis; all of whom when he was slightly better, he asked for. You see once again, someone suffering from dementia forgets that their parents are gone and often asks when they are coming to visit. Even Dad would tell me they had been in to see him. My grandad passed before I was born... It's just about answering those questions as sensitively as you can. Dad said to me often "What happened to her?" pointing to a photo of Mum, "Why does she not come and see me?" I would then have to tell him she can't because "She is in heaven Dad." I didn't want him to think Mum had abandoned him. They truly loved each other and Dad had supported her through her illness so gently and willingly. In this instance, honesty was the best approach.

It was the Linburn Christmas party on Wednesday 11 December. The staff suggested I take Dad down to the Bridge for it as he may like the lights and the music, even though he couldn't eat. So we went, but it was just too much for me. I fed Dad wee mouthfuls of his drink, talked him through the carols being played and pointed out the lights, but there was no joy in it for either of us and, I don't mind admitting, I was a wreck. It was so sad to see, and I wasn't doing Dad any favours by him being there or my crying, so we left and went back upstairs. It was much nicer being on our own and I felt that Dad needed to be afforded his dignity.

The next day Mr Guthrie came to visit. He knew it would be his last one and not easy to do but bless him, he was determined to do so. Dad was so very weak but we got him dressed and sitting in his big armchair on wheels, which meant he was strapped in for safety and was much easier to manoeuvre than a wheelchair. He looked smart in a bright pink polo shirt and grey tracksuit bottoms. He always suited bright colours and he was unusually bright mentally.

Gordon (the home manager) and the staff had told me he would have moments of lucidity he had not had for ages, and this was clearly one. He knew what was happening.

When I told him Mr Guthrie was here to say hello, Dad shot me a look as if to say 'you don't need to tell me who he is, I know!'. The visit was both happy and sad, but it meant so much to both of them, friends for over sixty years, but like the grandchildren before him, Mr Guthrie knew he wouldn't be returning. He is the only person to call dad Willy. I remember him doing so all my life. He leant in and said "It's time for me to go now Willy." Dad held his gaze, tears in his eyes and said in the faintest of whispers, "Goodbye." I think they both knew what they were saying. It was both a beautiful and so very sad thing to witness; two old friends saying goodbye to one another for the last time and even in the last few days of his life, Dad gave Mr Guthrie and I that beautiful gift of lucidity. I walked him to the door, we both cried but we knew what a wonderful friendship they had shared, something for us all to aspire to.

Lottie never did return to see her grandpa after that. The time had come for Dad to have my complete attention and I wanted to be with him entirely. On the Friday afternoon, Victor (another resident in Linburn but also a great chum to Dad) sat with us, him on one side holding Dad's hand and me on the other. Victor loved music and although he suffered from dementia, I think it was vascular, so he had days when he was very lucid — this was one of them. He sang to Dad, gently but beautifully. Everyone stopped for a while, it was a sight to behold. The three of us sat for a few hours, Dad dozing, opening his eyes on and off but the peace and tranquillity was soothing for him. Victor was upset too, he knew what was happening, we all did but we were just happy to be together. Later that afternoon Dad tried to say something to me. I couldn't make it out at first, his voice was so weak. I leant into him and what I heard; I could not believe. He looked at me, his blue eyes determined, and said "I'm worried about you." I told him not to be, he asked "Are you happy?" I nodded and said yes, to which he replied "Promise me," and I said "I promise you, Dad." He smiled and went back to sleep. Those were the last words he ever spoke, but they were the most beautiful ones and I will always treasure them. Even at his most weak he was STILL thinking about his wee girl and I knew then that he did know who I was. I can't tell you what that meant to me and even how astounded I was, but it does show you that someone as ill as Dad still had the capacity to care and for him, it must have been so important to tell me that.

The rest of the weekend was spent sitting quietly.

Bruce, Simon and Katie all came to visit and they gave me great strength in doing so. Dad had stopped eating and his fluid intake was minimal. He was becoming more agitated which was upsetting. I asked the staff if this was normal, to be told it was, but it was not nice to see. I also asked the dreaded question; "How long do you think it will be?" I was given the answer 'that Bill will decide'. At the time I found it almost incredible but I now know it to be true. I was not with my mum the last week of her life (as I was eight months pregnant with Molly and developed pre-eclampsia and told to rest) so I had not experienced the dying process and I don't mind admitting that I was really scared. Scared in case I let Dad down — would I know when it was happening? Would I be strong enough to do the best by Dad?

By Monday 16 December it was abundantly clear that Dad had entered into the final stage of the process. His breathing was very erratic, Cheyne-Stokes breathing it is called. He could go for a minute without breathing (I know this as I timed it while holding his hand), then letting out a big breath. He was increasingly agitated, and I was upset for him. I rang the buzzer; Alasdair came and could see Dad's agitation. We both knew what should be done for Dad's comfort. At 11.25 a.m. he started his 'end of life medication'. I did not consult Ainsley or Bruce; they had said previously whatever I thought was for the best was the right thing to do. Neither could be with Dad all the time because Bruce had lost his wife Carys the previous year and had three young children and it would not be fair for him to have to go through that again, and Ainsley was overseas. I did however call Bruce and text

Ainsley to let them know and both just said 'I hope he is at peace now'. It was an awful decision to make (another one) but I knew it was the right one.

In Erskine the room is filled with flowers by the home and made to look as lovely as possible. I went for a walk round the block with Si, who had come to join me. It was a surreal feeling. I knew there was no going back, but I also knew Dad was comfortable and that is all you can ask for in a situation like this. I also told the children what was happening. Max and Rosie did not say much, it was too painful. Molly on the other hand had lots of questions; some I could answer, some I could not. Bruce and Simon came in the evening and although we chatted to each other, we still made sure we included Dad in the conversation. They both went home but I was not going to leave Dad now. I sat beside him all night holding his hand, chatting, playing music to him. The funny thing was when I uncrossed my legs or made the slightest of movements, he would squeeze my hand ever so gently. It was almost as if he was just checking I wasn't going anywhere, quietly I told him as much!

Tuesday morning dawned and although Dad's breathing was even more erratic, he was still with us. I told him it was time to let go of my hand and retake Mum's, she had, after all, waited long enough to be reunited with her darling Bill.

Once again, the day was spent quietly listening to music and the boys came in to visit. It sounds strange but we all chatted away happily and although we all knew what was coming, if not when, we could see that Dad was at peace. Something he had never been while he was ill. I have talked about Dad's determination all his life and the way he fought this battle was no different. Very difficult at times to deal with but that was one of Dad's strengths, why should this be any different? So to finally see him resting was lovely. Bruce got up to leave and said "Bye, Dad, I will see you tomorrow morning." He asked if I was staying again and if I would be all right, 'yes and yes'! And we said we would see him tomorrow. Simon stayed with me. I got up to go to the loo and noticed Dad was almost foaming at the mouth so rang the buzzer. Help arrived in the form of Alasdair who had to suction the saliva from Dad as his throat must have closed over by this stage. We didn't witness that as Alasdair said it would not be pleasant to see but equally Dad would feel no pain.

The shift was changing and all the guys who had been on the day shift came to say goodnight, but I suppose it really was goodbye (in retrospect) to Dad. The love and care they showed not only to Dad but to me was so unexpected, but we needed it and I will never forget it. Simon stayed on with me and it was Ewa who was on night duty that night. She came to check on us at the start of her shift, Dad was peaceful. I had been checking his skin all day for mottling, a discoloration of the skin (particularly in the extremities) indicating the blood is not flowing there as it is needed elsewhere as death approaches. On Monday I could see it clearly but on Tuesday it was gone, and Dad's hands and feet were warm... odd I thought. About eight thirty that night I checked again, and I know Dad won't mind me saying this, but his feet were never his best feature and that evening they smelt! I told him I wasn't having him not looking his best, so I washed and talced them and put fresh socks on and made sure he was cosy. He was.

Suddenly his breathing sounded really bad. I rang for help. Ewa came with a new member of staff whose name I cannot remember, sorry. The nurse came and gave Dad an injection to make him more comfortable and they decided they would change him at the same time.

In the last two weeks of his life, I always left the room at this point to give Dad his dignity back, don't ask me why, I just felt it was important to do so. Simon and I stood outside his room for a couple of minutes then I heard Ewa call me to come back in.

As we entered the room Dad had gone a strange grey colour. I asked "What is happening? What is wrong?" Ewa said "This is it, Sarah."
I burst into tears and said "I'm scared, please don't leave me." Ever the practical Ewa, she told me to "Pull yourself together Sarah. Be strong, your father needs you!" That may sound harsh but that is exactly what I needed. I cupped my wee dad in my arms, told him I loved him and that it was OK to go. Ed Sheeran's 'Supermarket Flowers' was playing in the background... "When God took you back, he said 'Hallelujah you're home'". As my lovely daddy drew his last breaths in my arms, at 9.07 p.m., he opened his eyes and stared at a photograph of my mum, his darling Aileen, they were to be reunited in death. If I hadn't seen it for myself, I would not have believed it. When his last breath left his body, I sobbed like a baby on top of him.

His suffering was over, but selfishly I just wanted more time with my lovely daddy. But that's what it was, selfishness. Ewa told me she thought Dad's passing was beautiful and I hoped for him that it was. Looking back now, a year later, I can see that it was, but it still hurts. Simon kissed him on the brow and said "Bill you have the strongest, kindest heart of anyone I have ever met." Two beautiful men. It was fitting Ewa was there that night as she was the first person, Dad met on the Erskine staff, and she was to be the last.

I held Dad so tightly, then remembered I had phone calls to make: to Bruce who would call Ainsley, to Molly, Max, and Rosie. None were easy calls to make — although they knew it was coming, I don't think anyone thought it would be that night. The only offering I could give them was that it was so peaceful, so very peaceful. Often you might think those are words of comfort given to relatives who are not afforded the honour of being with their loved one at their passing for whatever reason, but I could honestly say it because it really was.

Simon and I sat with Dad for a few hours, funnily enough with a wee glass of white wine (Dad's favourite drink) and toasted him and all that he had given to us. I told him it was both an honour and privilege to care for him and one I would do repeatedly if I had to, and I meant that. I wanted him to wear his favourite jumper. When I asked him once why he liked it so much, he simply said "Because people speak to me when I'm wearing it." So simple but so meaningful to dad. Don't ask me why, I just needed him to be smart when leaving Erskine. I placed his wee squeezy ball in his hand, kissed him and told him how much I loved him. I packed up his photos and Billy the dog, and Simon and I left for home about one a.m. I don't think we spoke the whole way. Dad's journey with dementia was over and he too, had made his way home.

Chapter Thirteen
Miss Me But Let Me Go

The days following Dad's death were really a haze and they were a mixture of coping and a tsunami of grief that swept over me. They were also days for our family to be together and comfort one another; Molly returned from London on the Thursday and when we saw each other we both wept uncontrollably. Rosie just wanted to be at my side and Max couldn't acknowledge his grandpa's passing at all. Those days were of course also spent organising Dad's funeral. Although he was not religious, he understood the value of a service for those left behind, having been through loss himself.

It was all quite simple really; we would have a private cremation, then a service of thanksgiving at Mum's church and thereafter we were to go to his beloved Accies for a good old send off!

Between the three of us we put together what we thought was a lovely service, one that Dad deserved and also one for the carers who cared so lovingly for Dad at his most vulnerable, so they could learn more about him. Dad and I listened to Ed Sheeran's 'Supermarket Flowers' often — it is a beautiful song that talks about the passing of his granny and the love they had for each other, a life that has been well lived and that the reason you grieve so much is that you love so much too. I really connected with that song so we had it played on the piano and sung live in the church as the service began. My goodness, it was so sad but I know it touched everyone there (which I believe was about five hundred people… wow, all for our lovely dad).

Everyone knew of Dad's love of cricket, so Ainsley had this moment of inspiration where he suggested Soul Limbo by Booker T. & The M.G.'s be played as he went to make his tribute to Dad and also when we were leaving the church. Not ringing any bells? Well for the older generation, it is the theme music for 'Test Match Special', which Dad watched every time it was on. It really lifted the mood and Dad would have loved that.

Ainsley spoke of his memories of our dad and how he inspired and encouraged him to be the best he could be and see the world, but also of Dad's community spirit and philanthropy. It was beautiful, and I was so proud of him because Ainsley is not one to show his emotions readily.

Bruce gave me carte blanche with the flowers, which were a sea of blues, pinks, and whites.

Funny stories were told about Dad, loving ones about him and Mum, and happy ones of his children and grandchildren. As funerals go, I think it was a good one with some even writing afterwards (somewhat apologetically) that they 'enjoyed' it. No need for apologies, that is exactly what we wanted and what in fact, Dad wanted.

The title of this chapter is a song by the band Scrum, and it too really resonates with me. It talks of coming to the end of the road and the 'sun setting' for the person passing, of not crying "for a soul set free" and I suppose that is how it should be — Dad was set free.

My grief was only to begin but I know he wouldn't want me to be engulfed by grief, thus the reason for this book. I do miss my lovely dad immensely, but I have to also let him go. I'm not sure I'm there yet but I'm getting there. My mind and heart are full of a lifetime of memories and love for him, and I count myself so very lucky to have him as my dad for fifty years and the last four were some of the sweetest times, albeit some of the hardest too.

I do miss you Dad; my head is not bowed as low as it was a year ago and one day, I will be standing tall again because of the strength and love you gave me.

Chapter Fourteen
Silver Linings

It hasn't taken me a year to realise that there are so many silver linings I have taken from those last few years of Dad's life; I knew it then, as we were living them.

The most obvious and apparent one is the time we spent together. Dad and I had always been close, but this brought us even closer. Yes, there were times when he really did not like me and certainly did not trust me, but never once did I blame him for that — it was this awful illness talking and, if anything, I felt so sad for Dad that he had those moments when the red mist came down. Yes, I would walk away crying, but I never let Dad see me cry in those moments for fear of him realising he had upset me. Not once in a life that was so well lived and devoted to others, would Dad have been unkind, and I was not about to make him feel as if he had been now.

He told me family history stories I did not know and in turn I could recount them to him when he could no longer remember. We watched a lot of sport, joined the music therapy group, went on trips together and welcomed friends and family to visit. You cannot put a price on that. Time is the greatest gift you can give anyone I believe, and we both gave that to one another.

As Dad's illness progressed, he became ever more

reliant on me emotionally. Often, I would see him looking at me, never taking his eyes off me when we did have visitors, because he knew I would involve him in the conversations and even understand what he meant when no one else did. The trust that he had lost in me through fear and anger regrew and although at times it was so overwhelming and difficult to make the hard decisions, I surprised myself that I could. I look back now and think that Dad had that belief in me, in me? 'Pleasantly Plump' or 'Podge', as I was known to the family growing up. Bruce and Ainsley are both very successful businessmen, I was just a mum and housewife (although for a few years I couldn't even claim that title until I remarried!) But I suppose it is true, that when you are faced with adversity you find strength that you didn't know you had, and that's how it feels now.

Dad trusted me to come every day — I did. He trusted me with his personal care — I did it. He trusted me to feed him as you would a baby — I did. He trusted me to just sit quietly and hold his hand sometimes for hours — I did. But most of all he trusted me with his passing, making sure it would be as comfortable as possible for him and that I would remain with him — I did. To me, that he trusted me the way he did was an immense honour and although he never told me that he loved me, I always knew he did, but none more so, when he was at his most vulnerable.

I mentioned earlier that time is the greatest gift you can give someone, and I do know how lucky I am that I could spend all my time with Dad as I don't work — not everyone can do that. I often worried if the kids and

Simon were suffering by me not being home as much as before but they all to their credit understood, nay, wanted me to be with Dad as he was so special to them all, so I really appreciate their understanding. Mum had passed twenty-three years earlier, and in the last year of her life I worked part time so I could then give her my time for a few days but to also let Dad have some time off too. How many children can say they have been able to do that? I do not know, but I do know how lucky I am to have cared for them both when they really needed it and those times hold a special place in my heart. That was definitely the greatest silver lining of all time.

Another one, was all the wonderful friends I have made because of Dad going to live in Erskine, staff and residents alike. They become your family and support system and I definitely spent more time with them than I did my friends in that period. I can honestly say that my friends who are the carers are the most wonderful people I have ever met... unequivocally, the job these guys do is quite frankly amazing; dealing with dementia sufferers is not easy and Dad was certainly one who was difficult to handle — he fought that disease tooth and nail, approaching it like he did everything in life, with 100% commitment to fight it. As a result, he could be aggressive and uncooperative but the staff never gave up on Dad, finding ways to persuade him to do the things they needed him to do, such as washing. I honestly looked at them in awe. You cannot just become a carer, you are one, instinctively. I truly believe that based on what I saw in Erskine and in my friends. They all taught me so much; not just about the disease but also wee tricks to cope with Dad more easily. They were also there for me when I was struggling. It never crossed my mind that my lovely daddy would 'lose' his mind. There is a history of heart disease and cancer on both sides of our family so that was what I was expecting might happen to Dad in later life, but not this cruel Lewy bodies. As far as I am aware, no one in the family has had it previously, so I had no experience of it. To watch your dad lose the capacity to do anything, (right down to swallowing water in the end) is heart-breaking and at the time you just accept each failing stage, but it hurts so much and I cried so many tears. But there was always someone there to give me a hug and listen. I am and we are, as a family, forever in their debts for the way they cared so beautifully for Dad and us.

The residents are also a lovely silver lining because as I said previously, they and their families become your family too and I got to know so many of them so well. What wonderful lives they had lived and this wretched disease seemed such an unfair way to end their lives.

I remember one, Robert, (he rarely spoke and had been in Erskine for ten years I think) fought in the D-day landings — what an honour to know him! Robert would always wave at you when you waved at him, but as I say, rarely spoke. On a few occasions though, he would beckon me over to him and ever so quietly tell me he had been watching me with Dad and he would tell me what a lovely girl I was… that really touched me.

Victor, I have mentioned before. He was such a character and although he and Dad were ostensibly quite different, they were in fact very similar, both sharing a deep love of family and both had great senses of humour. Victor was visited often by his two brothers, Phillip and Kenneth, and often the two families would sit around and chat, each learning about one another, which for me was lovely to hear their stories too. Dad really enjoyed that. The two of them would go to the activities together, each giving one another comfort by doing so and each enjoying their favourite tipple (red wine for Victor and white wine for Dad), it was lovely to see. As Dad deteriorated, Victor and Kenneth would give me a sense of comfort as we all had spent so much time together, and there was no doubt they were hurting too. That's the thing with dementia and indeed death, it is a real leveller.

Peter was another lovely man (they all were). I only name those who Dad and I were particularly close to. I remember Dad and Peter both enjoying Katie's cherry cake (cherries removed of course!) on Dad's birthday. They just looked like two old friends remembering better days. His lovely wife always asked after me too, not just Dad, yet she was in pain too. Peter was cognitively good so he knew what was happening and every day he would ask "How is Dad today?" It made me feel so sad that he truly knew the reality and, although residents would rarely see a fellow one who had just passed, leaving Erskine (I for one never saw anyone, it is done so discreetly), Peter knew the score.

I feel honoured to have not only met all these wonderful people (too many to mention by name) but to have spent so much time with them and their families, at a time in all our lives when the overwhelming emotion was sadness, but somehow, we all still managed to smile. That is testament not only to Erskine but all those 'who sailed in her'.

This brings me onto yet another silver lining. Dad's awful illness gave me a sense of direction that I suppose I was needing. I had just seen my last child, Rosie, off to university when Dad became quite unwell, so I seemed to slip from mum to carer seamlessly. But what would I do thereafter when the worst would happen?

I learnt so much about dementia in that time; observing all the carers and asking questions (I wanted to give my best to Dad as after all, he had always done his best by me) that I realised this was where I wanted to be; to volunteer and also raise awareness and money for Alzheimer Scotland and I promised Dad this is what I would do. We so desperately need to find a cure, or even something to halt the progress of this hopeless and debilitating disease, which has the ability to dismantle the sufferer but then give them a radically slowed down death over a period of months, which, if you make to the end of the journey like my lovely Dad did, was a drawn-out ending. He wasn't himself but he was powerfully present.

Dementia is often described as 'the disease of the century' — the time bomb exploded long ago, more of a demolition job. Yes, we care and understand those who suffer from it and they are no longer hidden away but we must as a society do more, after all no one is spared from this disease. Death comes to us all in the end, but I can honestly say I fear dementia more than the 'Big C' — if not for me, but my children. We now have the 'Big D', having lost a parent to both.

The impact to those suffering, and their families, cannot be underestimated. Dementia is such a cruel and long farewell and I truly believe there were a lot of

moments when Dad was scared; scared of what
happening and scared because he had no control ove
I too was scared, because I could not only not sto
rampaging through his mind and body, but I also fear
how bad it may become. It was worse than I feared, b
it was because of that I resolved to try and do somethin
to help stop this menacing, creeping disease.

Lottie was all set to be the pet therapy dog at Erskine.
I was all set to help in any way I could as a volunteer and
to visit other care homes and purely just sit quietly,
holding a hand of someone who perhaps didn't have the
family that Dad and others had.

I was thinking about organising a charity ball in aid
of Alzheimer's, but in early February 2020, Covid hit.
Boom. The whole world stopped and any plans we had,
and still have, are out the window. Covid has decimated
care homes (don't get me started) and the families of
those living in them. I worry too about my friends who
work there, what horrors must they have seen? Yes, death
is a fact of life in residential care, but not on this scale.
Our social care staff are so grossly undervalued, but they
have shouldered most of the weight of this pandemic and
they have done it willingly. Do you know why? It's
because they love their jobs and their residents. We owe
it to them as a society to find a cure for dementia as well
as those we have lost to it.

Dad's passing when he did is itself a silver lining. I
cannot imagine not being able to spend most days with
him, holding his hand on our journey together, to be able
to comfort and love him. The very nature of the disease
tells you that if you suffer from it, you would not

was
r it.
it
ed
ut
g

family cannot come to visit. You
ıbandoned. And for some that is
ıed and they simply gave up. What an
ʝour life, one that was so valuable, but
ɔf your family until the last few hours. I
κy that Dad did not have to feel that and
ʲovid, you have wrecked so many lives, but
ou arrived too late to ruin Dad's last few
ılver lining indeed.

ʲten said that death can be a friend, an end to
ʲing, but when your loved one does go (in my
ıd) you just want them back. Just a few more days
ɪ his hand and chat to him a bit longer, so the last
ɪs aren't the last words. But that is for me, he had
ʲered enough. Dad can watch the Test matches, and
ʲ Nations with Mum again, spend time with his mum
ınd dad and brother and sister again. All the people he
asked for so often as he became more ill. He can get back
to all the things he loved doing and did so well. The
Numbers Mann is working his financial wizardry on
businesses and charities who need him, his mind is clear
once more and his brain awash with calculations. The fog
has cleared, and I for one am glad that Dad is back to his
wonderful, caring, fun, gentle self. He is looking down
on us all with a massive sense of pride and love. I can feel
it. But we, in turn, are all looking up to him feeling the
same.

He gave me the strength and inspiration to write this
book, something I never thought I could do, but I was
able to do it 'because I know who he is', my wonderful
dad.